Welcome aboard!

This is Pip, the youngest pirate on the ship.

Solve the puzzles in this book and help Pip find the buried treasure.

Look out for Pedro the parrot too. You'll find him in every picture!

While the other pirates are fast asleep, Pip is busy cleaning the pirate ship.

Can you help him
find his mop?
Can you spot
these things?
the captain's hat
three mice
a teddy
bear

Pip washes all the pirates' dirty clothes.

Can you match the pairs of socks?

Can you spot these things?
two seagulls
a fishing net
a bucket

Pip even cooks the pirates' dinner!
One dinner is different from the others. Can you spot the three differences?

Can you spot these things?
a loaf of bread
three candles
a spider

Pip and his friends are trying to catch some fish for dinner.

Which pirate has caught a fish?

Can you find these objects?
three blue fish
a boot
three starfish
What has Pip caught?

Pip has caught a treasure map!

Can you help him find the path from the dock to the red cross? That's where the treasure is buried!

The Tallest Tree
Crocodile Lake
Can you spot these things?
a magnifying glass
a crocodile
an anchor
13

"I'll need the little rowing boat to find the buried treasure," says Pip.
Can you spot these things?
two seals
two crabs
a telescope

Which ladder should
Pip climb down to
reach the boat?

Pip and Paws set off for the island in the rowing boat.

Can you help them get there safely?

Can you spot these things?
a crab
two dolphins
a whale

There are monkeys everywhere on the island!

All the monkeys are the same colour except for one. Which one is different?

Can you spot these things?
a bunch of bananas
three blue flowers
a snake

"We need to cross the lake if we want to find the treasure," says Pip.
Can you spot these things?
a banana
two baby monkeys
three crocodiles

Which bridge should they use?

"The treasure is buried under the Tallest Tree," says Pip.
Can you spot these things?
three butterflies
two coconuts
a snake

Which path leads to the treasure?

The chest is filled with gold coins and sparkling jewels!
The monkeys have found four more pieces of treasure. Can you find them too?

Can you spot these things?
two bananas
a leopard
a tortoise

Pip is a pirate hero –
he will never have to
cook or clean again!

Can you find the pirate twins?
Can you spot these things?
a chocolate cake
three lanterns
a flute

Answers

Pages 4-5

Follow the red line to find Pip's mop.

Pages 6-7

The matching socks are connected with lines.

Pages 8-9

The plate on the right has three differences that are circled in red.

Pages 10-11

The captain has caught the fish!

Pages 12-13

Follow the red line to the treasure.

Pages 14-15

The ladder on the right leads to the boat.

Pages 16-17

Follow the red line to the island.

Pages 18-19

The circled monkey is a different colour.

Answers

Pages 20-21

Pip needs to cross the bridge in the middle.

Pages 22-23

Follow the red line to the treasure under the Tallest Tree!

The monkeys have taken the items circled in red.

The twins are circled in red.

More pirate fun

Pirate day

Try dressing up as a pirate for the day. Tie a bandana around your head, wear a stripy T-shirt and make a cardboard sword. Maybe you could even host a pirate-themed party!

Pirate ship

Draw the outline of a simple pirate ship. Colour it in with pens, paints or crayons. Then draw some pirates or a ship's cat, cut them out and stick them on the ship. Display your finished artwork on the wall!

Treasure hunt

Just like you helped Pip find the treasure, you could make your own treasure hunt! Hide a treasure in your home and get a friend to hunt for it. You could write a series of simple clues to lead them to it. For example, the first clue could be 'Look somewhere very cold' and the second clue could be hidden in the fridge. The final clue leads to the treasure.

Make your own pirate flag

Use paper, cardboard, felt or fabrics to design a pirate flag. What do you think should be on your pirate flag? Can you find a pirate flag in the book?